Poems from Eden

www.**booksattransworld**.co.uk/childrens

POEMS FROM EDEN
AN EDEN PROJECT BOOK : 1 9039 19045

First published in Great Britain by Eden Project Books,
a division of Transworld Publishers

PRINTING HISTORY
Eden Project edition published 2002

1 3 5 7 9 10 8 6 4 2

Set in Perpetua
Eden Project Books are published by Transworld Publishers,
61-63 Uxbridge Road, London W5 5SA,
a division of The Random House Group Ltd,
in Australia by Random House Australia (Pty) Ltd,
20 Alfred Street, Milsons Point, Sydney, NSW 2061, Australia,
in New Zealand by Random House New Zealand Ltd,
18 Poland Road, Glenfield, Auckland 10, New Zealand,
and in South Africa by Random House (Pty) Ltd,
Endulini, 5A Jubilee Road, Parktown 2193, South Africa

Printed and bound in Great Britain by
Cox & Wyman Ltd, Reading, Berkshire

Poems from Eden

Annamaria Murphy

Illustrated by Alan Clarke

CONTENTS

Acknowledgements

All the poems in this book are by Annamaria Murphy except
for the following, which were written in collaboration with
Eden colleagues Dr Joanna Readman and Mike Andrews:
What am I? (p. 25); *Tea: Where Have You Supped and Who With?*
(p. 52-5); *Hemp* (p. 57).

The poems in the first section, Songs of Eden, were originally
commissioned for the Eden opening ceremony. Inspired by
Bill Mitchell, Artistic Director of the Kneehigh Theatre, they
have now been recorded as songs with music by Jim Carey
and sung by a mass Cornish choir.

1
SONGS
OF
EDEN

Eden
(Man)

If I were to build
What would it be?
A table for all my wordly goods?
A house
A palace
A tower
To lock myself within?

And if I were to dig
Where my feet stand,
What would I find?
A pot of gold
Mud
Clay
Roots

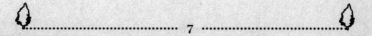

Or other men's stories?
And like them
What shall I become?
Legend
Memory
History
Or,
A man of clay
Which my own hands
Have dug.

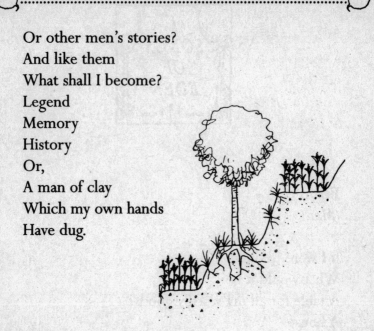

Washing
(Adam and Eve or Treve and Bryn or Sharon and Mark)

As yet,
We have not been
Washed
Not wanting to
Rub off the mark
Of our very own
Original
Sin.

We bare the first
Designer label.

Garden of Babel,
Cain and Abel
It
All
Started
With
Us.

We are new
Our skins blush-pink
Under the mud.
Caked
Half-baked.
Shaken,
We have not
Yet
Been
Stirred.

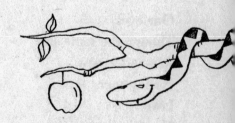

Experience

Skin.
We've grown into our skin.
Whereas before
Parts of us just didn't fit.

There was only
Light.
And no story
Except for
Innocence.

Our hearts,
Though always here,
Beat now with more rhythm
And louder
Sometimes
Than the roaring sea.

Our eyes,
Though the same size
Are wider now
Having seen
Love
Come and go
and come again,

Having seen
Fruit
Rot
And grow
Into
Trees
Higher
Than expectation
Even.

Our hands,
Though no broader
Can hold more
And let go
Things more slippery
Than Water,

And when we've found our sea legs
Our clay legs
Our rock legs,
We shall stand firm
Against all storms
And crafty winds.

You see
We've grown into our skins,
Stretched tight
Over experience
And bones
And –
Things will never be the same
Again.

Strange Fruit

Black roots
Red fruits
Scorched seed
Sweet mead.

Juice
That stains skin
Like
Sweet sin.

Chocolate
Dark Rivers of it.

Vines that twist
Like serpents
Wines that intoxicate
And promise love
Where love is not.

Hands that
Cut the crop
But taste not
The Flesh.

Spices
That flavour
History
Bitter.

Wit
Dry as bones
Song as thick as cream.

The sea
Land licking
Roaring
Boiling with fish
Seducer
Widow maker.

Land that meets the sea
Heather and gorse
Air that smells
Of salt and coconut.

Coffee
Sleep stealer
Wheeler dealer
Cash crop
Shop till you drop.

Foreign brides
On Cornish shores
Mango
Guava
Saffron
Love as ripe
As aching peach
The last fruit
Out of reach.

One bite
Would be just right.

Temptation
Hope
Pandora's Box
Eden dug from Clay.

Birth

First Breath
Defies death
From blue
To grey
Like night
To day.

There's mud
And blood
And unweathered skin.

Pink as dawn
The first born.

Into their mouths
Clean of all words
And song
We breathe
Thought
And dreams
And love
And fight
And desire.

Pink as dawn
The first born.

They grow to feel
The forest floor
They smell
Gorse
And sea
And fruits
That taste
Of sun
And fire.

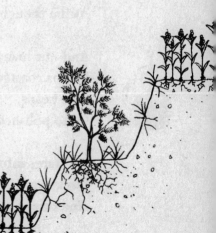

2
HUMID
TROPICS

Madame Café – a story of unrequited love

'Madame Café
I am your slave!'
Said the man.
'You make my hands shake
My knees quake,
My heart beat.
Oh, my sweet,
I cannot sleep
At the thought of you!'

And our man
Weeps roasted tears,
Like beans,
Onto polished tables.

He stares into Madame's
Dark eyes
And cries

'You are my morning
My night
My afternoon
My waking dream
I love you
Black,
White,
And with cream!'

 'I love you
Freeze dried,
Powdered,
Granulated,
Hot, Iced.'

And his cries
Became louder
And louder…
Louder than
The clink of cups
And the gurgle of tills.

Across the world,
His cries become a breeze
His sobs,
A whisper through leaves.

'Give me peace,'
Cries the man,
'Let me rest,'
As the night folds in,
As dark as coffee,
A woman picks her last bean.

Exhausted
She sleeps.

Welcome Explorers All!

Welcome explorers all to the Humid Tropics

Meet Madame Wealth
    Doctor Health
        Mother Nature
            Lady Bountiful
                Beauty and the Beast
                The World's Feast

                    Weather Machine
                    Fragile Queen

                        Forever Green?

Rainforest Sound Poem

Beaked flowers sweating rain,
Lung-shaped lilies breathe mist.
Mimosa dusts hummingbird.
Pear-shaped fruit births cashew.

Calabash balloons from branch
Whilst guarana winks.
Papayas cling to trunks.
Pink-fleshed guavas.
Trees drip with healing
And flavour.
Crooked-billed Macaws sing.

Felled trees scream.
Forest people speak their lives.
Rainforest.

Rainmaker

Trunks, drunk with water
Leaves breathe clouds
Clouds cry rain
Roots drink rain
Trunks, drunk with water
Leaves breathe clouds
Clouds cry rain
Roots drink rain.

No trees
No leaves
No leaves to breathe clouds
No clouds to cry rain
No rain
No drink for roots
No roots
No trunks
No trees

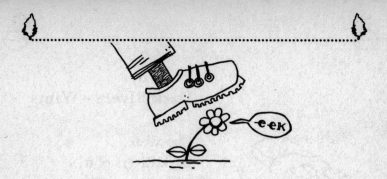

Rubber

Rubber Blubber Bounce Flounce
Wind it Stretch it Throw it Sit on it

Wear it Tear it Wear and tear it Love with it

Stick with it Play with it Protect with it
Float on it Drive with it Ride on it
Keep dry with it Stamp on it Rub out with it
Rub shoulders with it
Rubber stamp it

Dark Rivers – Wants

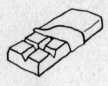

Chocolate,
Dark Rivers of it.
Sweet liquid silk.
Centres soft with
Strawberry, lime,
Coconut cream.
After dinner
Morning sinner.

Luxury,
Hot creamy comfort.
And,
Underneath the foil,
(Gold, silver, emerald)
No trace of soil
Or toil.
Feed
Our

Need,
Satisfaction
Is
Guaranteed.
Chocolate,
Dark Rivers of it.

Dark Rivers – Needs

Cocoa,
Dark roots of our trees
Their shoots wait for nourishment
The soil yawns
Black spot
Witch's Broom
Strangle leaf
And stem
With wicked embrace

We need
New seed
To feed your need

Dark Rivers – Rainforest

Its dark voices
Its tongues speak
Of
Wildness
And difference

If we listen
It will feed us
Heal us
Sustain us
And give us chocolate,
Dark Rivers of it

What am I?

Wipe your feet on me
Plant your seeds in me
Wash your hair with me
Drink a toast with me

Fairground prize
Monkey's eyes
Horse's hooves
Mother's milk

I'm a sweet treat
White fleshed
Creamy, dreamy
Girls in bikini
Taste of Paradise.

AM, MA and JR

Polly is Saturated (or the palm oil shopping list)

Tub of Marg
(Easy spread
On budget bread)
Rubber gloves
(Hands like doves)
Soap
Rope
Soap on a rope
Wine
(The cheapest)
Pills
For morning after
When I'm feeling Ropey.
Ropey
Soapy
Dopey.

Lip stick
(Ruby red)
Candles
(Romance and bed?)
More wine
(For tongue loosening)
Red lips
(Fatal kiss)

Too much wine
Near miss.

Pudding?
Choccy-woccy
Chocolates
Hard centre?
Strawberry slick?
Ice-cream?
Rain forest dream
Toffee sludge
Coffee fudge
(Fat on hips –
Just won't budge)

Pastry
(low fat for my waisty)
Crisps
(potato wisps
Prawn?
Cheesy-weesy?
Lemon and beef?)
Oily-moily
Lunch-box filler
Crunch
Munch
For our lunch.

Stain remover
(From spilt wine)
Last night's love
Scrub with glove.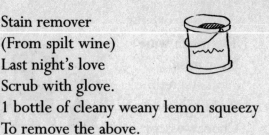
1 bottle of cleany weany lemon squeezy
To remove the above.

Tin of Beans
Oven chips
With not much fat
(Fancy that!)
Oodles
Of pot noodles
For quiet night in
More choccies
(It's not a sin)

Scrubby wubby
The bath tubby
Toilet duck
(For yucky muck).
Shampoo
(that mends split ends)
Massage oil
In case I get lucky
Hand cream
(Peach dream)

Holiday brochure
For palm fringed
Sun tinged
Breakofalifetime
Sunsettingonlocalchildbearerhandycraftmakers
Souvenir
Bargain hunters.
Price slashers
Cost Cutters.

Toilet paper.

Get the gist of this shopping list?

Only 4 items do not contain palm oil.
Can you guess which?

Palm

Leaves explode
Against sky
A hairy armed
Muscle bound
Stout
Slender
Firework of a plant

A high rise
Bottle-necked
Wolf-backed
Bristled trunk
Bearded
Smooth skinned
Family of a plant

Leaves
Green tongued
Eyelid veined
Cleopatra's fans

Trunks
Helter-skelter
Leaves shelter
Profit maker
Life giver.

'Cross our Palms'

'Cross my Palm Trees
With Silver,'
Says Alvera,
'So I may shoe these
Tender feet'
As the oily money
Slips from her
Hands
Onto our lips
Hips
Stock market tips.

'Plant my forest
With gold,'
Says May Lie,
'And bottle
Its blood
Into fantastic
Plastic.'

'Clean my trees
Of buzzers
And stingers
And on the wingers,'
She says,

'So we may grow more
And not be poor.'

And then they wipe
The morning dew
With its chemical hue
With their palms
As tender
As mothers
Everywhere.

Bamboo

Slender dancer
Bird boned
Iron strengthened
Double jointed
Scaffold Skele

Homemaker
Whisper-still
Tiger striped
Lacquer stemmed
Green veined
Cool beauty
Music maker
Heat giver.

Flora Beauteous

Tiger-lipped lemon Orchids
Cradling lily petal protecting
High-rise stamen

Rude-tongued Flamingo Flower,
Twisted delicacy of tight-furled *Hibiscus*
Sweet kiss of ruby-red lipstick flower,
Corkscrew, snail-shell *Begonia* leaves
Lizard-foot *Croton*
Red Hot Cats' Tails
Tease Zebra Plant
and Butterfly Lily.

Trumpet-flowered *Hippeastrum*
Announces
Orange hairdoed *Marantacea*
Blood-coloured *Margot*
Shocks
Shameless *Orchidaceae*

Jacob wears his coat
Danger red.

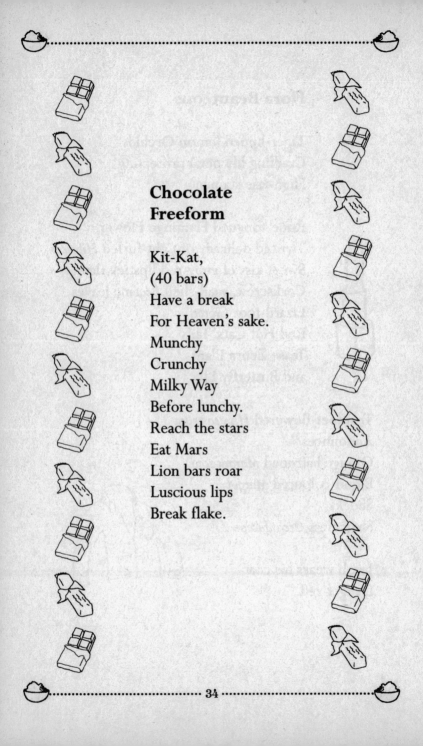

Chocolate Freeform

Kit-Kat,
(40 bars)
Have a break
For Heaven's sake.
Munchy
Crunchy
Milky Way
Before lunchy.
Reach the stars
Eat Mars
Lion bars roar
Luscious lips
Break flake.

A moment alone
With a Toblerone.
A posh date
With an After Eight.
Women's guilt
Child's bribe
Soldier's ration
Seducer's passion
Dark mint
Cognac hint
Soufflé
Gateau
Bedtime drink.

3
WARM
TEMPERATE

Introduction to the
Warm Temperate Biome

Salutare! Enter all –
The Lands of the Warm Temperate Regions
Discover:
The Mediterranean's Paradise
California's Horn of Plenty
South Africa's Garden
History and Olives
Oranges and Dust
Fertile Deserts
Culture's Cradle
Born of Sister Fire and Brother Drought.

Mediterranean Landscape

Dust dry
Fire singed
Lemon-scented land
Made by hand
      Grey-gaze
Silver blue
Heat haze
Root maze
      Heart's desire
Olive
Rock
Myth
Fire

Olive Trees

Olive trees
Are the old men
Who once sat under them
And picked their fruit.

They sit in clusters
With puckered faces
Like salty black olives
Veins on arms
Like bark
On their sheltering tree.

Holiday Destination

Holiday destination
People infestation
Ouzo Boozers
Ibiza nights

Fig Tree

Silver-tongued Temptress
Eve's blush
Sticky fingered
Dark juiced

Cacti

Spiny-backed Gorgons
Spike-toothed
Thick-tongued
Croc-skinned
Snake dancers

Who am I?

I am
Christmas
Summer
Bottom of the stocking.

I am ration book memory
Cold comforter
Small sun
On a grey day.

I am
Bridal blossom
Travelled
Painted
Sainted.

I am Spanish lady
America's baby
I have blood
And navel
Skin
And seed.

Answer: Orange

Who am I?

I am flavour
Sailor's saviour
Cleany-weany
Lemon squeezy.

I am
Peeler
Healer
Wheeler-dealer.

I am
Tongue-tipper
Lip zipper
Gin sipper.

I am doctor's helper
Plague ridder
Neck sweetener
Nose gay.

I am
Saucy
Bottled
Pickled
Love bitter.

Answer: Lemon and lime

Olive

Within me lies:

End of the flood
Light's blood
Survival seeker
History's keeper

Inside of me find:

Medicine chest
Heart's rest
Blood cleaner
Hair redeemer
Lover's liquid
Skin smoother

Under the cover discover:

Wealth Oil
Health Oil

Travels with My Nose

Breathe In...
  India
    Incense
  China
    Fish and jasmine
  Spain
    Coffee and oranges
  America
    Bagels
    Burritos

First love
    Malt and after-shave
    Sweat and almonds
    Wood-smoke and sea

Childhood
    Wet duffel coat
    Beeswax
    Liquorice
    Dettol sting
    Coconut seaweed
    Bunk bed comics
    Sago
    And done-to-death
    Cabbage.

Making Scents?

Making scents?

Calvin Klein
Musk Devine
Poison Paloma.
Christian Dior
(Opens the door)
Red Bull
(You can always pull)
Denim
Sporty

Deep Blue
Aqua
Splish Splash
(Makes a dash)
Isis
Athene (Goddess of Love)
Zeus
And Minotaur
(Gods from above)
Rive Gauche's Ghost
(It's hardly there)
Eastern Promise
(Never kept)

Addiction Obsession
Impact Possession
Brut Endurance
With Action Impact

The Old Spice Team
Catch Cool White
Lynx.
Fcuk
There's NOdebate

Toujours
On a Moonberry Musk
Silk Nights
In Paris.
Pastel Fresh
In lace
Cleopatra's Juice
For Eternity.

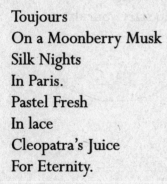

Lagerfeld
Duty Free
Romance with
Dolce Gabbana's
Baby Doll.

The Jazz
Allure
of Rive Gauche.
L'Homme
and
All Woman
Under an Anaïs Anaïs
Sun, Moon and Stars.

On a pine fresh
Lemon zest
Odour decoder
Morning.
To start your day

Pine

I am mountain green.
I am wipe clean.
I am Christmas needles.
I clear the head,
I am foxes' bed.
I am crisp, clear.
My leaves,
Winter's tear.

Tree

My roots
Are in
Underworld,
Where worms crawl
And men fall.

My trunk
Is in Middle Earth
Where men talk,
Live and walk.

My branches
Reach heavenward
Towards the blazing sun,
And men try
To reach the sky
But —
They cannot reach
As far as I.

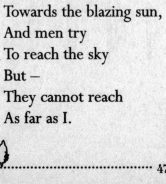

Perfect

Perfect veg
For the perfect life. Not bent,
Easier on knife.

Time saver.
Less strife.

Pre packed
Pre washed
Sliced
Diced ... Nice.

Cauliflowers,
White
Tight
Bright.

Carrots,
Smooth
Straight,
Each one
The same weight.

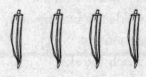

Life style
Cook-book slave.
Mangetout
All the rave.

Roadside Veg – Penzance

We are roadside veg...
We are bent orange
Hook-nosed
Dirt clumped
Fat
Thin.

We are...
Creamy yellow
Loose floreted
Broccoli
Cauli
Anarchic Queens.

We are…
Bulbous
Knobbled
Tubered
Apples of the earth.

We are
Straight from the soil.
Savour
Our flavour.

Veg with Airmiles

Out of season?
That's no reason
For us not
To reach
Our destination.
Strap us in,
We can be flown
from any nation.

Consumer trends?
We'll make nature bend.
Our only wish
Is to grace your dish.

Petits pois
(Not too far)
Aubergine
(Very keen)
Star fruit,
Pineapple
Lychee
(Very chi-chi)

You see,
We are veg with attitude.
We'll fly at any altitude
To make your culinary
Wish
Come
True.

Tea: Where Have You Supped and Who With? A.M.

I have drunk tea
Brewed by the women
Who picked it
At the end of their day
And the start of my night.
I have drunk tea
After birth
And it tasted like

Nectar.
I have had tea with
Milk,
Sugar,
Jasmine and Mary.

I have drunk
Ceylon in Ceylon,
And Darjeeling in Darjeeling.

I have had it
Green,
Black,

White,
Red,
And Golden.

I have drunk it from
Porcelain,
Bamboo,
And Clay.
I have cried into it,
And had my future read from it.
I have drunk it
When I haven't wanted it,
And when I'm desperate for one.
I've drunk it with Russian sailors,
Tibetan monks,
Shivas,
Divas,
Grandmothers,
Vicars,
Lovers,
Friends.
In my dreams
I've had a nice cup of tea with —
The Queen,
Attila the Hun,
Elvis,
Nelson Mandela.

I've had it –
Hot, iced and spiced.
I've drunk it in the air,
Up a mountain,
On an elephant,
In a train,
And
Tea
At
Sea.
Tea, Tea, Tea.
Will You Share A Cup With Me?

M.A.

I have had tea with
Great aunts using silver teapots – milk in first
and little finger crooked
Cucumber sandwiches
A Pasha's daughter, in a glass set in filigree gold
Low-bowing white geishas
Bearded Uzbekis smoking hubble-bubble pipes
Sympathy
Condors flying overhead
Crumpets
Argentine gauchos with peg teeth – but that was
mate green tea from a silver straw
A force nine gale blowing

Half my mouth numb from dentist's novocaine
A chainsaw in my hand
A hand over my mug, sitting round a camp fire
in India under a banyan tree.
Every time the leopards roared near by the
langur monkeys crouching overhead
peed themselves.
An Ethiopian princess
Poetry
Woolly gloves on
A heavy heart
Rancid yak butter
Haste
A cat on my knee
War and Peace
The first girl I kissed
The skipper of a trawler in a North Sea gale —
and I threw it up
A string orchestra
The ghosts of my dead friends
Spring sunshine
A KGB Intourist guide
Cavers in New Zealand, filming a moa skeleton
A thermos in China
Janet in the kitchen at 4.30 p.m.
My keyboard, writing this.

Beer

Beer.
Froth,
Yeast,

We drink a toast
To our golden host,
Black beauty,
Tongue loosener,
Belly giver
Song maker.

Foam on lip,
Hand on hip,
Drown your sorrows
Like there's no tomorrow.

Father and son
Are one,
Saturday night streets flow
With the golden glow
Of
Beer.

And,
Remember,
'There's nothing so gloomy, sad or drear
 As to stand at the bar
In a pub with no beer.'*

*(Australian drinking song)

Hemp

Animal feed
Ice-cream
Margarine
Bags
Tags
Rags
Shirts
Socks
Building blocks
Canvas sails and ships' ropes
Tough clothes and bank notes
Oils and cords
Insulation boards
Varnish to stop tarnish
Lubricants and garnish
All this and much more — from one plant — hemp.

AM, MA and JR

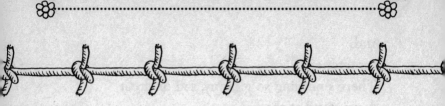

Ties that Bind

Ties that bind
Fish to net
Sail to ship
Flag to pole
Tent to ground
Horse to post
Child to tree,
Kite to holder
Boat to harbour,
Ties that bind.

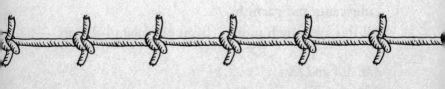

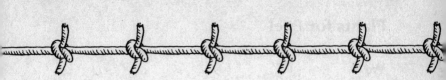

Knots

My stomach's in a Knot
Because of you.
It's a Turk's Head-Sheepshank-
Fisherman's Half Hitch-Anchor Bend.
You gave me the Slip-Knot,
And I'm twisted up like a Cat's Paw.
Oh! Won't someone throw me a Bowline?
A Log Hitch, or a Jug Sling?
My legs swing like a rope-bridge,
So,
Please someone,
Throw me a line,
A Monkey's Fist
Or a Turtle Knot,
And
Save
Me
From Drowning!

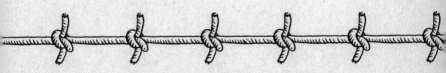

Plants for Fuel

We
Chop it
Dig it,
Mine it,
Drill it,
Pump it,
Harness it.

Then we
Burn it,
Boil it,
Warm by it,
Cook with it,
See by it,
Drive with it,
Fly with it.

Can we
Treasure it?
Explore it?
Save it?

Reading

Today
I have read
All day.
Words dance
Like Dervishes
And re-arrange
Themselves
To fool
My eyes.
I fall into the book
And become
Black
And
White.
And,
When the words shout out
I cry
And paper is turned
To pulp.
Sentences
Are washed away
On salt rivers.

Today

Words

fool

Black

White

shout

cry

This
Tends to change the story
Somewhat.
Reading.
I cannot stop.

Reading

stop

Sunflower

Bee seducer
Flower Medusa
Healer
Tall as halls
Sun-eater
Toxin drinker.

I am the dawn's
greeter
I am engine juice
Dribbled
Nibbled
Painter's muse.

5
WILD CORNWALL

Wild Cornwall

Granite makes fist from hedges
Bracken as brittle as weasel's laugh
Lean-to hawthorn
Gold brown wind waving
Pale pink gold
Fern in constant curtsey
Lichen gloves rock
Heart stopping
Delicious melancholy
Where the land meets the sea
Bird quivers over prey
Moss explodes on rock.

My Grandmother Said (1)

My Grandmother said
If I don't go to bed,
The woodman will get me,
And I'll be dead.

My Grandmother Said (2)

Campions make your blood stop,
Eat a dandelion, you'll wet the bed.
Sloes make your eyes pop,
So everyone says.

Witches fly on ash stakes
(I've seen it for myself)
Venus favoured birch,
So everyone says.

If you don't put your Allen Apple
'Neath your pillow,
You'll be left in the lurch,
So everyone says.

It must be true,
Ivy berries
Are the Devil's poo,
Nettle tea is
Witches' brew.
It must be true,
Everyone says.

Heathland Palette

Red?
No
Brazen bronzes
Bruised crimson
Burnt umber
Deep wine burgundies
Heather proud with purple
Dawn pinks blushing

Brown?
No
Rusts
Chestnut golds
Hot orange that burns eyes
Wild cat black.

Grey?
Nah!
Shy silver
Sea-spray whites
Yellow creams on fungus fans.

Green?
Nope!
Cat's eye emeralds
Moss of Green Man's cloak
Jealous lichen limes.

What am I?

Skin slasher
Wool catcher
Wind-wise Old Man's Beard
Tree forlorn
Painful beauty
Hidden booty.

Answer: Hawthorn, Crataegus monogyna

Gorse

Butter yellow
Sharp as Stiletto
Smell of coconut
And salt.
I am barbed
But soft
I wag in the wind
With agreement
Till your back is turned.
I can be blood bringer
Tear wringer

I make a Cornishman cry
At the memory
Of me
Fire desires me
I am the Gold
Of the Black and Gold.

Lichen

Shed for me
Tears of sorrow,
'Here today,
Gone tomorrow.'
Lichen *Heterodermia isidiophora*.

Rose

I am Rose
Everyone knows.
I am
Preened
Pruned
Plucked.
I am
Cultivated
Sophisticated
Cherished
Beloved
Noticed
Painted
Sainted.

Scented Rose

Nosegay
Lovers' way,
Cleopatra's dream.
My petals lay
On Street,
Bath,
Bed.

My precious oil
Is squeezed
And teased.

Western Rustwort and
Heterodermia Lichen

We are lowdown
Green laced
We are rock skin
Clay kin
Unsung
Unhung

Pollinators

Long tongued-
Short tongued-
Snout nosed-
Bees,
Butterflies,
Beetles,
Hawkmoths…

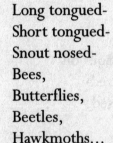

Dine on –
Nectar à la Carte,
Pollen Fricassée,
Propolis Flambée…

From –
Cuckoo Pint,
Eyebright,
Meadow Clary,
Apple Blossom,
Periwinkle,
Fennel…

Who are Perfumed and Dressed in –
Purples,
Pinks,
Oranges,
Blues…

Under Me (Path poem – from the path's point of view)

Under me
Are
Roots
And
Shoots.

They push
Against
Their stone roof
With all their
Twisted
Might,
To find their
Way
To
Light.

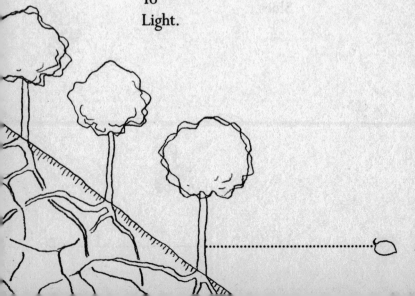

They find
My cracks
And crevices
And,
Try as I may
I cannot
Keep
Them
Under
Me.

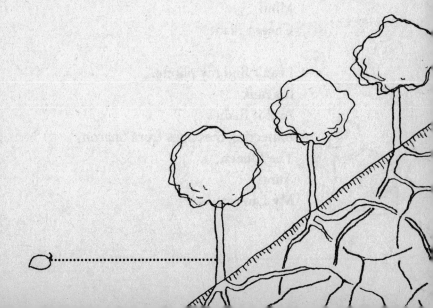

6
VISITORS' CENTRE

Lost Property Poem

'May we help you?'

'Yes please!
I have lost my
Glasses,
Hat,
Keys,
Wedding Ring,
Husband,
Mind,
Cheese Plant.

I can't find my phone.
It's pink
And it flashes.
Expecting messages from Sharon,
The Queen,
Aunty,
My Lawyer.

Can't find my car.
It's Beige
And I parked it in
Apple,
No,
Mango,
Banana?
Fruit salad?

Oh help!
I need a coffee,
The lavatory,
A bus,
A lift
My husband.

What does he look like?
He's tall
And I last saw him
In the
Warm-Humid-Temperate
What do you call them?
The things that look like
Bubbling milk,
Flies' eyes
The Diamond on my wedding ring?

A guide book?
Ah thank you,
Yes please
You've been most helpful …
Excuse me,
I'm sorry,
But I can't read
It
Without
My
Glasses.'

Friends of Eden

'Meet me for coffee,'
Said the friend,
'and we shall sit
where poets sat
and talk of love
and life
and art.'

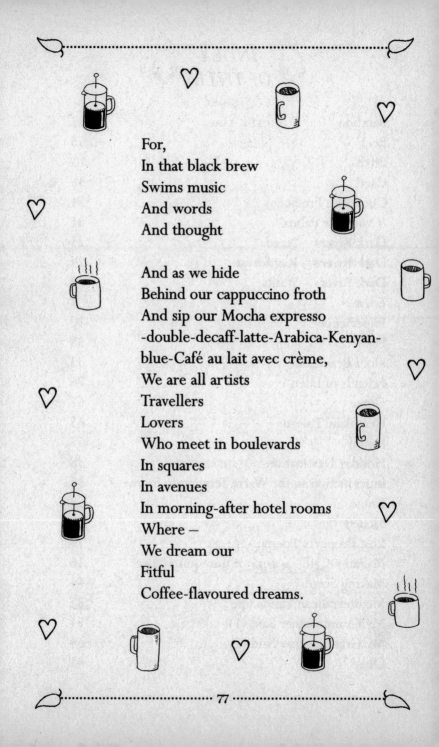

For,
In that black brew
Swims music
And words
And thought

And as we hide
Behind our cappuccino froth
And sip our Mocha expresso
-double-decaff-latte-Arabica-Kenyan-
blue-Café au lait avec crème,
We are all artists
Travellers
Lovers
Who meet in boulevards
In squares
In avenues
In morning-after hotel rooms
Where —
We dream our
Fitful
Coffee-flavoured dreams.

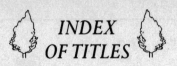

INDEX
OF TITLES

INDEX OF FIRST LINES